CW00959742

'Nan McCoo and the Birthday Bother' is the second in a series of
picture books, based on Steven's much-loved 'McCoos'. Developed
and written by Shirley Husband, and illustrated by Maurice Hynds
of See Saw Creative, they are magical tales of family and friendship,
to remind children how beautiful and colourful life can be.

Can you spot Bonnie McButterflee?

If you had a Nan like oor Nan McCoo
What a lucky wee person you'd be
She's aye there for cuddles and sorting oot muddles
She's a fine Scottish granny ye see

One day there was Nan, looking after her clan
In her colourful kitchen of clay
T'was a special occasion, the oven was blazing
And the smells were amazing you'd say

She was starting to bake a magnificent cake
For Chloe, for her birthday tea
"Wee Chloe's my pet, I just want her tae get
A wee treat, so she'll think lucky me!"

She finds the right page, "this cake's all the rage
it's got rainbows and unicorns too"
So she straightens her pinny, then gives a wee whinny
"Yer trippin' me up Davy – shoo!"

Wee Davy's her dug, with a right cheeky mug
And he thinks that he's in for a treat
He just loves an egg, so he's starting to beg
And he's getting right under her feet

Nan softens the butter and stirs in the sugar
And creams them together 'til pale
When she cracks in the eggs, Davy's up on his legs
And crivvens he's starting to wail

She sifts in the flour, as she looks at the hour
The family will all be here soon
Once she's put all her love in, the cake's in the oven
And she whistles a cheery wee tune

Now the cake's golden brown, and it's cooled right down
The beautiful icing's all done
It's got pinks, it's got blues, it's got yellow there too
Every colour that's under the sun

The McCoos all turn up for a wee bite and sup
In the kitchen, where they know they'll be
Treated like kings, to rare, glorious things
So they beam as they sit down for tea

"Yer in for a treat, c'mon take a wee seat"
Says Nan as she gives them a hug
But who's that doon there, lurking under the chair
Oh no, it's wee Davy McDug!

Shhhhh!

He hides, then he jumps, there's a thud, then some bumps
And the spread, well it all hits the deck
And Nan's hopping mad, as she yells at our lad
"Davvvy, I'll wring your wee neck!"

She chases him here and she chases him there
She thinks that he's ruined Chloe's tea
But Chloe's so sweet, and the scene's such a treat
That they all roar with laughter and glee

For if you had a Nan, like oor Nan McCoo
What a lucky wee person you'd be
She's aye there for cuddles and sorting oot muddles
She's a fine Scottish granny ye see.

Glossary

Did you understand all the colourful Scottish words and expressions in Nan's story? If you need some help, here's oor Chloe with a glossary!

oor – our
wee – little
aye – always/yes
oot – out
clan – family
t'was – It was
pet – a name for someone you love
tae – to
all the rage – in fashion
pinny – apron
yer – you're
shoo – get away
dug – dog
mug – face
crivvens – gosh
sup – drink
doon – down
hits the deck – falls on the floor
lad – boy